TOWN & ~

Logbook

DS

Birdwatching Tips

The aim of this series is to encourage you to look out for the birds around you, and record when and where you see them.

It is important to get to know how a bird moves, flies, and sings as well as identifying the shape, so the illustrations are there to show you important features to look out for, and the accompanying text tells you how the bird behaves.

Becoming familiar with common birds allows you to spot rarer sightings, so this book is to help you practise your birdcraft and enable you to become acquainted with the birds in your area and beyond.

Contents

Birdwatching Tips 3
Robin 5
Bullfinch 6
Wren 7
Blackbird 8
Chaffinch 9
Long-tailed Tit 10
Nuthatch 11
House Sparrow 12
Dunnock 13
Quick ticklist 14-15
Great Tit 16
Jay 17
Blue Tit 18
Magpie 19
Goldfinch 20
Wood Pigeon 21
Sparrowhawk 22
Barn Swallow 23
Greenfinch 24
Fieldfare 25
Green Woodpecker 26
Chiffchaff 27
Brambling 28
More birds 29
Notes & Sketches 30-31
Index 32

Erithacus rubecula

Body length: *12-14cm*

Where to spot:

Shrubs, vegetable beds,

hedges, small trees

Resident

Robins are probably one of the first birds we get to know, with their red breasts and affinity with Christmas. They are also bold and territorial, and will spend time defending their patch from other Robins.

Males and females look the same, and youngsters are brown and spotty, developing their characteristic colouring as they mature.

A Robin has a beautiful, slightly squeaky song, melodic and with lots of verses. The alarm call is a series of ticks, either singly or running together.

Date	Notes

BULLFINCH

Pyrrhula pyrrhula

Body length: *15-17cm*

Where to spot:

Fruit trees, hedgerows,

wooded areas

Resident

A Bullfinch's white saddle is often the main identifying feature as it flies off in front of you. The male's bright pink breast is only noticeable in good light; the female's breast is a khaki brown. They share white wing bars and rump, and they are often in pairs or flocks of a few birds.

They like to nibble on fruit tree buds but it's always a delight to see them among the apple branches even if the crop is slightly lessened.

Listen out for the call: it's a rather melancholy whistle.

Date	Notes

Troglodytes troglodytes

Body length: *9-10cm*

Where to spot:

Dense shrubs, nooks and

crannies

Resident

For such a small bird (about the size of a ping-pong ball) the Wren is a pint-sized powerhouse. They are tiny, really tiny and move in a staccato, jerky manner, with tail cocked upright. Wrens are unmistakeable as they cross over the garden low to the ground, with whirring wings.

Both sexes look the same, and youngsters are spottier than their parents.

They have a loud song: a clear trilling melody and the sharp tack of an alarm call from the centre of a thicket is bound to be a Wren.

Date	Notes

BLACKBIRD

Turdus merula

Body length: *23-29cm*

Where to spot:

Lawns, shrubs, trees,

lamp posts, walls

Resident

Blackbirds are easy to spot, with their handsome black plumage, bright yellow beak and eye ring. They have a slightly jerky movement, and hop or walk along the ground, stopping frequently to watch and listen for worms.

The females are a milk chocolate brown with a dark beak. Young Blackbirds are a spotty version of their mother and are easily confused with a thrush.

The song is delightfully rich and tuneful, and their alarm call is a series of short sharp "plinks" followed by a flurry of notes as they fly away.

Date	Notes

Fringilla coelebs

Body length: *14-16cm*

Where to spot:

Shrubbery, borders, small

trees, grassy areas

Resident

CHAFFINCH

A very pretty bird: a salmon-pink front and grey head, with prominent white bars on the wing that make identification simple as it flies off with its characteristic undulating flight. They feed on seeds and insects, making them often seen in gardens and parks.

The female has the same white wing markings, but is khaki green to the male's pink; she can look a bit like a House Sparrow.

The song is tuneful, starting with a few "pinks" followed by a descending warble.

Date	Notes

LONG-TAILED TIT

Aegithalos caudatus

Body length: *13-15cm*

Where to spot:

Trees, shrubs, scrubby

undergrowth

Resident

Long-tailed Tits are teeny-tiny (half their body length is tail!) but their shape and habit make them difficult to miss. They flit through branches in family groups of around 10-12, twittering conversationally to each other and displaying acrobatic prowess as they investigate branches for tasty morsels.

Males and females share the same plumage of pink breast and black eyebrow banding a white forehead; juveniles have a dark head. The long tail is black with a white strip along its length.

Date	Notes

Sitta europaea

Body length: *12-14cm*

Where to spot:

Large trees, deciduous

woods

Resident

Bold and aggressive, and the black eyestripe coupled with the characteristic pose of wide stance with beak up (showing the pale chin) makes the Nuthatch unlike any other bird you might see. They hop up and down trunks with ease looking for invertebrates.

The males and females are similarly coloured, but the female has a paler rusty-brown bottom, making the white spots look more pronounced on the darker male.

They are vocal birds with a wide variety of calls including short sharp sounds and a quizzical "dwee-dweee".

Date	Notes

Passer domesticus

Body length: *14-16cm*

Where to spot:

Eaves and roofs, hedges,

shrubs, trees

Resident

The archetypal cheeky 'LBJ' or Little Brown Job, House Sparrows are familiar birds as they have long inhabited the same space as us, nesting in our buildings and sharing our lives.

Sparrows are a striking combination of black, white, grey and rich brown with a stout beak, used for eating seeds and grain, and they often flock together in large groups.

Their song is quite simple: chattery and conversational, with a rattly buzz when alarmed, and lengthy bouts of repetitive chirps when they are courting.

Date	Notes

Prunella modularis

Body length: *12-14cm*

Where to spot:

Hedges, brambles and

scrubby areas, borders

Resident

DUNNOCK

Although a Dunnock is about the size of a Robin, it has a very different habit, mooching around on the ground in among shrubs, looking for their preferred food: insects. They have beautiful colouring: slate-grey and stripes of black and brown. Although they look as though they could be confused with a sparrow, they have a much daintier beak, and tend to pair up rather than gather in flocks.

Dunnocks have a pleasant quality to their song, and often perch atop a hedge or small tree to deliver their melody loud and clear.

Date	Notes

Use this page as a quick ticklist

Date completed:

GREAT TIT

Parus major

Body length: *13-15cm*

Where to spot:

Large and small trees,

shrubs, orchards

Resident

The bright yellow breast and black and white head make this sparrow-sized tit an easy spot. They eat insects and seeds so often frequent gardens and parks.

The female has a narrower, patchier black stripe down her chest, and her yellow is a little more muted, but apart from that the sexes look the same. A young Great Tit's plumage is basically a greyish yellow all over.

They have a cheerful upbeat song, including a two syllable "ti-cha ti-cha" as well as "pinks" like a Chaffinch.

Date	Notes

Garrulus glandarius

Body length: *32-35cm*

Where to spot:

Oak trees, wooded areas

and open ground nearby

Resident

Our most colourful crow, the Jay plays a part in planting trees as it gathers acorns and other tree seeds in its mouth and buries them to eat during the winter. These forgotten stores grow into new woodlands.

The white rump and wing markings are distinctive as they fly; Jays are never far from a tree and their flight is rather laborious and flappy. The glorious iridescent feathers on their wings are sometimes seen as a flash of electric blue.

Their song consists of a coarse warning screech as well as a wide array of mimicked calls of other birds.

Date	Notes

BLUE TIT

Parus caeruleus

Body length: *10-12cm*

Where to spot:

Woodland, gardens,

orchards, allotments

Resident

The yellow and blue plumage is attractive and familiar, so these tits are one of our most well-known birds. They are remarkably acrobatic, and will suspend themselves every which way (including upside down) to access tiny morsels like ants and aphids from buds and bark as they hop up and down the branches.

The male sports brighter feathers than the female, and young Blue Tits have yellowish cheeks.

Their song is a high-pitched "si-si-si-si" often moving in to a longer trill.

Date	Notes

Pica pica

Body length: *40-50cm*

Where to spot:

Trees, villages, roadsides,

lawns, open ground

Resident

MAGPIE

The black feathers change from glossy green to iridescent blue depending on the angle, and the white breast and wing bar set off these stunning feathers beautifully. The tail is longer than the body, and is often raised as the bird struts around open areas looking for worms, insects, and other meaty treats such as roadkill and carrion.

Difficult to say it has a song, as most noises are harsh and rather shouty. The rapid-fire alarm call when spying a cat or bird of prey is usually effective at deterring the predator.

Date	Notes

GOLDFINCH

Carduelis carduelis
Body length: *12-13cm*
Where to spot:
Borders, small trees and
orchards, pine copses
Resident

Exotic plumage coupled with skilful handling of prickly plants to extract the seeds make spotting a group, or 'charm' of these fine little birds a delight to see. Red and white face with a flash of golden yellow in the wing, and dots of white on the black feathers.

Juveniles lack the bright head colouring of their parents, but share the long pointed bill used like a pair of tweezers on thistles, teasels, dandelions, and other seed-rich plants.

Their song is a bubbly, buzzing twittering conversation as they chat amongst themselves while they forage.

Date	Notes

Columba palumbus

Body length: *38-43cm*

Where to spot:

Woods, gardens, large

trees, lawns and fields

Resident

WOOD PIGEON

Up close, as we can often get to these large and familiar birds, the beauty of Wood Pigeons becomes apparent: they have a beautiful soft grey-pink breast and pale grey head, with a sheen of silver-green above the white neck patch. Extraordinarily accomplished in flight, they are often mistaken for birds of prey, and show their prowess in flight with a characteristic climb-and-swoop manoeuvre.

As well as the distinctive five-syllable cooing call, they also clap their wings as they clatter through branches when alarmed.

Date	Notes

SPARROWHAWK

Accipiter nisus

Body length: *29-41cm*

Where to spot:

Hedgerows, gardens,

trees, shrubbery

Resident

As the name suggests this bird of prey will take small birds, although anything up to the size of a pigeon is on the menu, ambushing them in a flurry of feathers and alarm calls. It flies fast, hugging the vegetation hoping to make a strike with its needle-thin legs.

As with many raptors, the male is much smaller than the female, and he has the rusty-red colouring over his barred chest whereas the female is grey and white.

Their call consists of a chattering cackle, but they rarely speak outside the breeding season.

Date	Notes

Hirundo rustica

Body length: *17-21cm*

Where to spot:

Open fields, village

greens, ponds

Summer visitor

BARN SWALLOW

Skimming low over fields and ponds catching flying insects, Swallows are well-known for their astonishing migration and ability to return to the same nesting area each year. The lengthy tail streamers of the male are the most obvious feature.

Landing to collect mud for their cup-shaped nest is one of the few occasions these birds venture to the ground, preferring to stay in their aerial comfort zone, either flying high, or perching on wires and chattering and burbling excitedly to each other.

Date	Notes

GREENFINCH

Carduelis chloris
Body length: *14-16cm*
Where to spot:
Wooded areas, bushes
and shrubs
Resident

A chunky finch, with green and yellow dominating its plumage; the yellow wing bars are particularly evident in flight. A Greenfinch's heavy beak is used for eating large seeds and nuts.

The male has the brightest colouring, with the female being altogether more understated.

This finch has two songs, although one can hardly be called that: it's a buzzy wheeze, whereas its actual melody has a Canary-esque quality with lots of whistling and trilling notes.

Date	Notes

Turdus pilaris

Body length: *22-27cm*

Where to spot:

Berry and fruit trees,

hedges, fields, lawns

Winter visitor

FIELDFARE

This large thrush visits us from Scandinavia in October through until February in order to feast on our berries and fallen fruit, often gathering in large numbers alongside migrating Redwings.

Distinguishable from Song and Mistle Thrushes by their light grey rump (which can look silver in low winter sun), brown cape, and bright white armpits.

They have a distinctive, slightly squeaky "chacka-chacka" call as they fly off from the tree, as well as sounding out a rattly alarm when chasing corvids.

Date	Notes

GREEN WOODPECKER

Picus viridis

Body length: *30-36cm*

Where to spot:

Mixed woodland, fields,

lawns, grassy areas

Resident

Although this species nests in tree holes, they feed mainly on ants meaning they spend much of their time on large lawns and paddocks, flying up when disturbed with a strongly undulating flight.

The green feathers with the red head are a distinct and colourful combination. As with our other woodpeckers, the Lesser and Great Spotted, their four toes are set with two facing forwards, two backwards unlike most birds; this allows for a good grip on trees.

They issue a shrill "kyu-kyu-kyu" when they take off.

Date	Notes

Phylloscopus collybita

Body length: *10-12cm*

Where to spot:

Hedges, deciduous wood-

land, garden trees

Summer visitor

Across most of the country the Chiffchaff appears in March, and on a cloudy day these birds can look a bit insipid, but with some sunshine on the plumage, the yellow and khaki-green hues look fresh and bright.

Warblers migrate from their warm winter territories of the Mediterranean and sub-Saharan Africa as they are insect eaters, and have to follow the food.

It sings a cheery "chiff chaff chiff chaff" although some get a little out of rhythm with a few extra chaffs and chiffs in the sequence.

Date	Notes

Fringilla montifringilla

Body length: *14-16cm*

Where to spot:

Large and small trees,

shrubs, hedges

Winter visitor

An 'orange Chaffinch' is how a Brambling is often described, being of similar shape and size. They breed in Scandinavia during the summer and visit us in the winter to consume beech mast and other seeds.

The call is an enquiring, upward inflection "dweep?" with a slight nasal tone, and they tend to stay in their groups (sometimes hanging out with other finches as they move across the landscape foraging), so you are more likely to see and hear Bramblings en masse.

Date	Notes

More birds you may see:

STARLING

HERRING GULL

NIGHTINGALE

WAXWING

JACKDAW

*You will find
these in the
other books
in the series*

Notes & Sketches

Notes & Sketches

Index

Barn Swallow 23

Blackbird 8

Blue Tit 18

Brambling 28

Bullfinch 6

Chaffinch 9

Chiffchaff 27

Dunnock 13

Fieldfare 25

Goldfinch 20

Great Tit 16

Greenfinch 24

Green Woodpecker 26

House Sparrow 12

Jay 17

Long-tailed Tit 10

Magpie 19

Nuthatch 11

Robin 5

Sparrowhawk 22

Wood Pigeon 21

Wren 7